SFX-10
CHRISTMAS
SONGS

C000136419

FOR ALL HOME KEYBOARDS

SFX

Exclusive Distributors:
Music Sales Limited
8/9 Frith Street, London W1V 5TZ, England.
Music Sales Pty Limited
120 Rothschild Avenue,
Rosebery, NSW 2018,
Australia.

This book © Copyright 1985, 1991 by Wise Publications
Order No. AM39686
ISBN 0-7119-0679-3

Music Sales' complete catalogue lists thousands of titles and is free from your local music shop, or direct from Music Sales Limited. Please send a cheque/postal order for £1.50 for postage to Music Sales Limited, Newmarket Road, Bury St. Edmunds, Suffolk IP33 3YB.

Your Guarantee of Quality
As publishers, we strive to produce every book to the highest commercial standards.
All the music has been freshly engraved and the book has been carefully designed to minimise awkward page turns, and to make playing from it a real pleasure.
Throughout, the printing and binding have been planned to ensure a sturdy, attractive publication which should give years of enjoyment.
If your copy fails to meet our high standards, please inform us and we will gladly replace it.

Wise Publications
London/New York/Sydney

The ABC of SFX Music

In SFX music, the melody is clearly written in large lettered notes. Each note can easily be located on your keyboard and then played with the right hand.

The songs in SFX music books are all written in the following keyboard range. The symbol at the beginning of the music staff is the treble clef, indicating the notes are played with the right hand:

The Keyboard

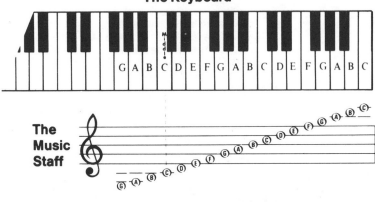

The Sharp Sign (♯) will sometimes appear before a music note. Simply play the *black key* to the *right* of the *white key:*

Example: C♯   **Example: F♯**

The Flat Sign (♭) placed before a note tells you to play the *black key* that lies to the *left* of the *white key:*

Example: E♭   **Example: B♭**

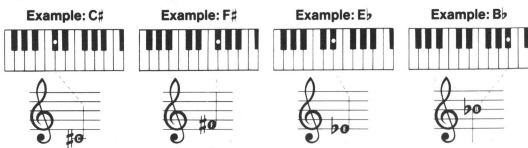

The Music Staff is divided into equal sections by vertical lines called *Bar Lines.* Each section is a *Measure.* The end of a piece of music is marked by a double bar line.

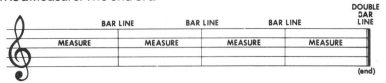

All music is played in time to a *beat.* The six types of notes most often used in SFX music all have a *time value* that relates to the beat:

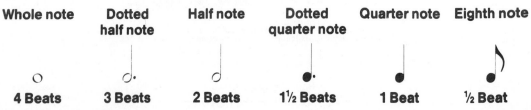

Whole note	Dotted half note	Half note	Dotted quarter note	Quarter note	Eighth note
4 Beats	3 Beats	2 Beats	1½ Beats	1 Beat	½ Beat

The Rest is a silent break in the music. The symbols are written in the staff, and like music notes, rests each have a time value:

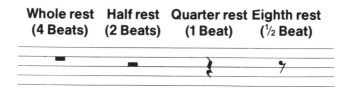

| Whole rest (4 Beats) | Half rest (2 Beats) | Quarter rest (1 Beat) | Eighth rest (½ Beat) |

The Time Signature comprises two numbers at the beginning of the music, after the treble clef sign. The top number shows the amount of beats in each measure. The bottom number indicates the type of note that will receive *one* beat. These are the most popular time signatures. The lower number 4 represents the quarter note:

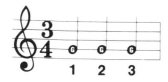

1 2 3

1 2 3 4

The Tie is a curved line that connects two consecutive notes on the same line or in the same space in the staff. When a tie appears in the music, play the first note and sustain the sound for the *total* time value of the two notes:

Tied Notes

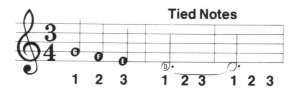

1 2 3   1 2 3   1 2 3

Repeat Signs are two dots alongside double bar lines. They indicate that all the music in between the pairs of repeat signs is to be played through again:

Quite often there will only be one repeat sign at the end of a passage of music. The repeat is then made from the very beginning:

Double Endings are sections of music with staff repeat signs. 1st and 2nd time brackets above the staff indicate where a short 'skip' is to be made in the music after the repeat has been played:

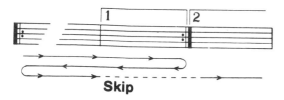

Skip

Left Hand Keyboard Accompaniment. SFX music has Major and Minor chords clearly written above the staff. The optional 'seventh' type of chord is shown with the 7 outside the chord frame:

Your keyboard Owner's Manual will explain how these chords are played with your left hand.

Conventional (Fingered) Chords can also be used. **The SFX Master Chord Chart** in this book shows the most practical chord positions for this type of left hand accompaniment.

We Wish You A Merry Christmas

Traditional

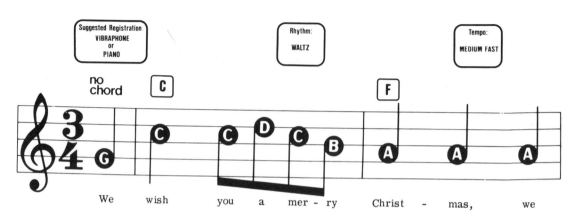

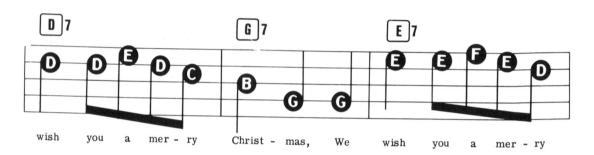

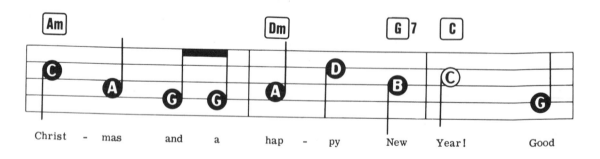

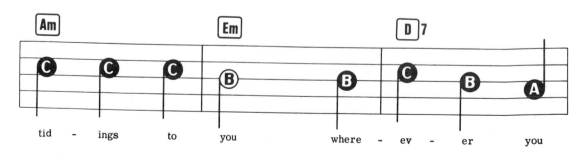

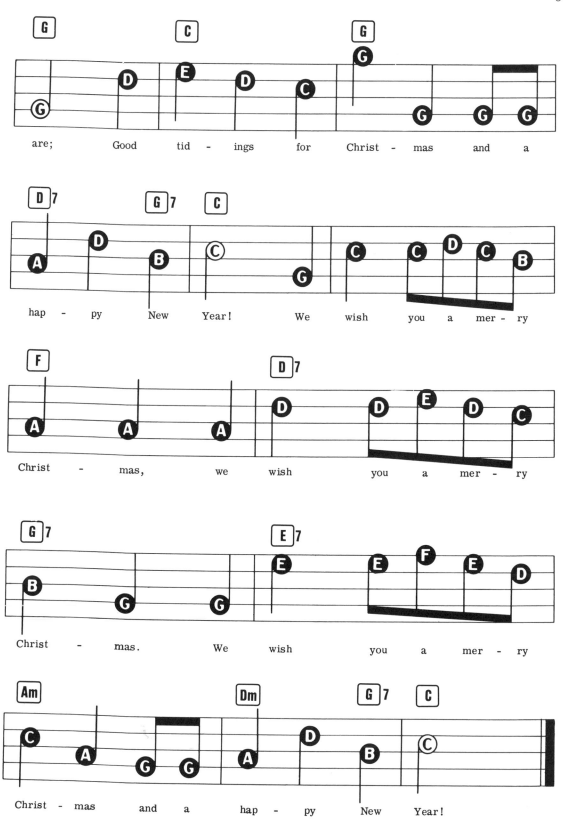

Snowy White Snow And Jingle Bells

Words & Music:
Billy Reid

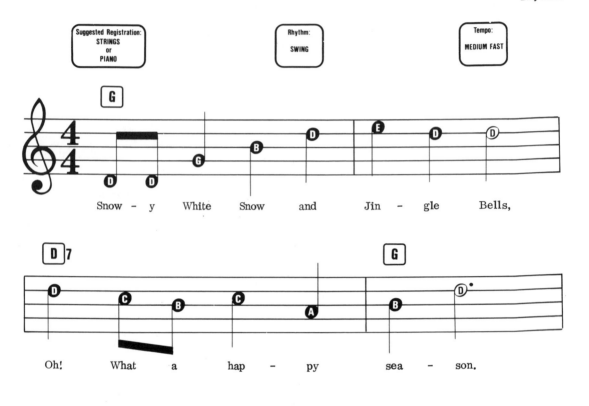

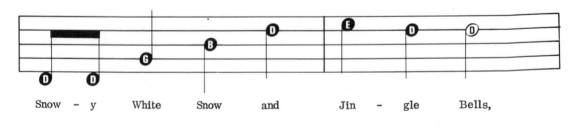

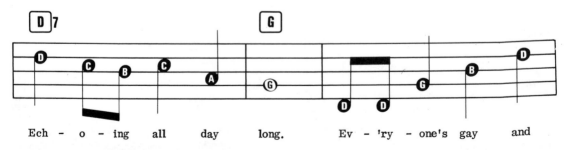

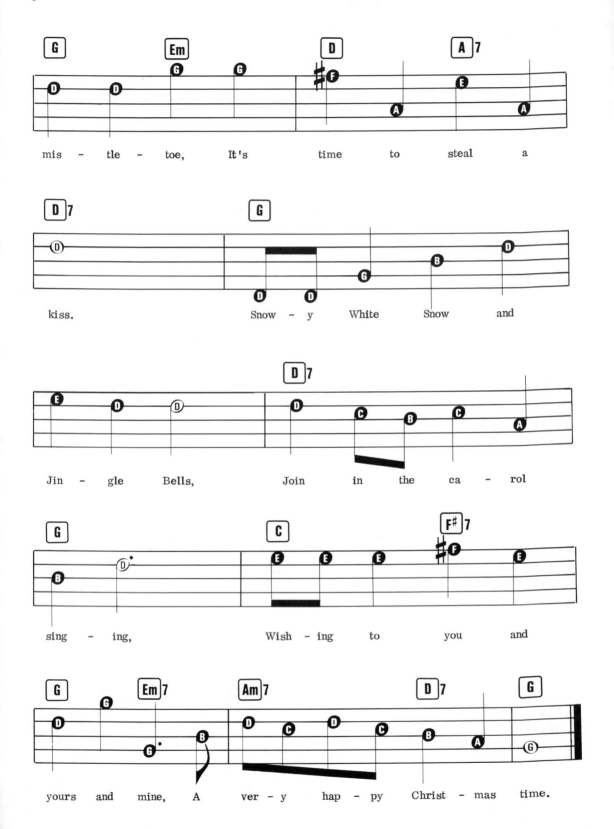

Frosty The Snowman

Words & Music:
Steve Nelson and Jack Rollins

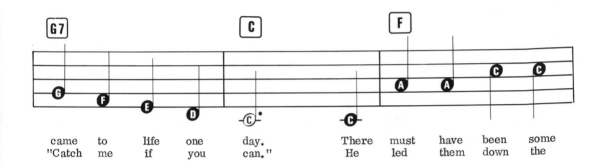

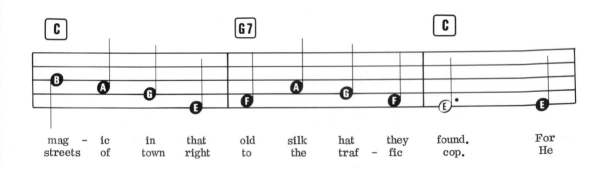

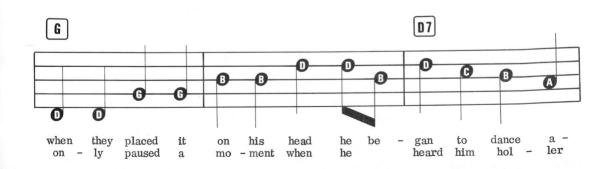

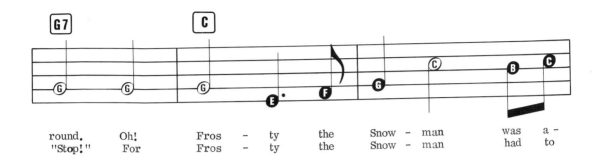

round. Oh! For Fros - ty the Snow - man was a -
"Stop!" For Fros - ty the Snow - man had to

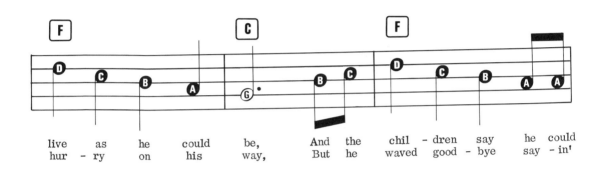

live as he could be, And the chil - dren say he could
hur - ry on his way, But he waved good - bye say - in'

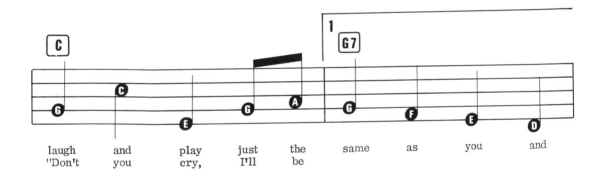

laugh and play just the same as you and
"Don't you cry, I'll be

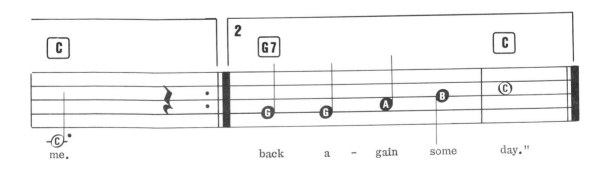

me. back a - gain some day."

Silent Night

Traditional

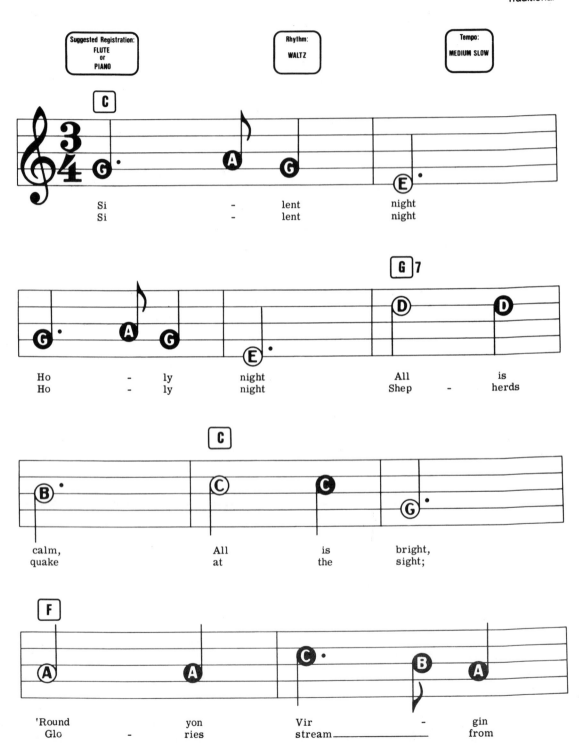

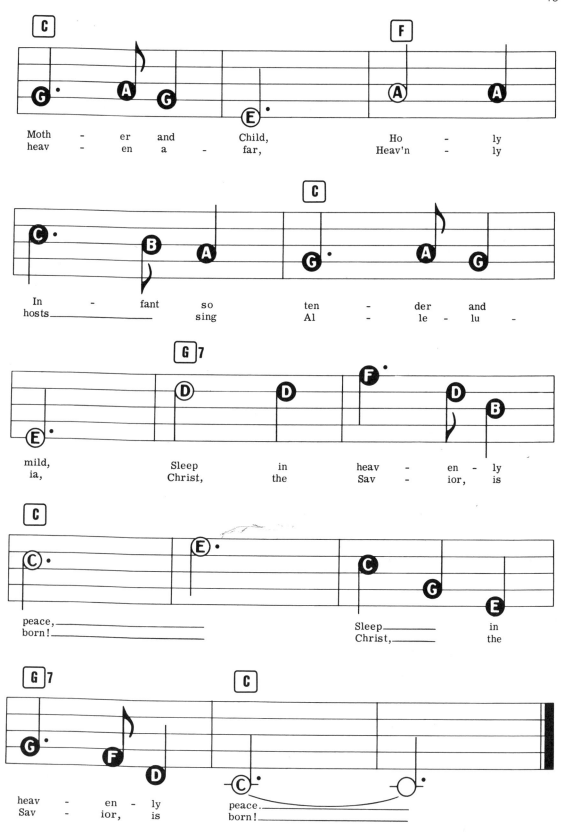

God Rest Ye Merry Gentlemen

Traditional

Suggested Registration:
BRASS
or
PIANO

Rhythm:
SWING

Tempo:
MEDIUM FAST

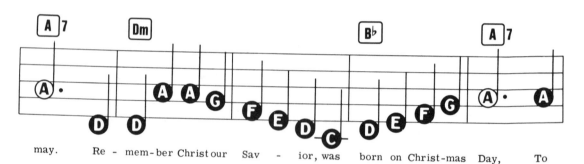

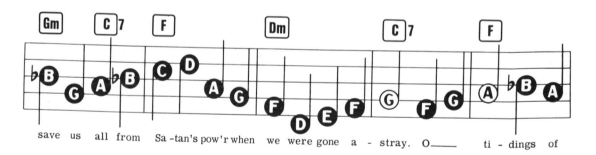

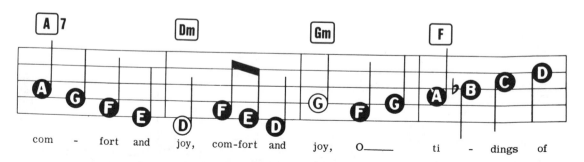

15

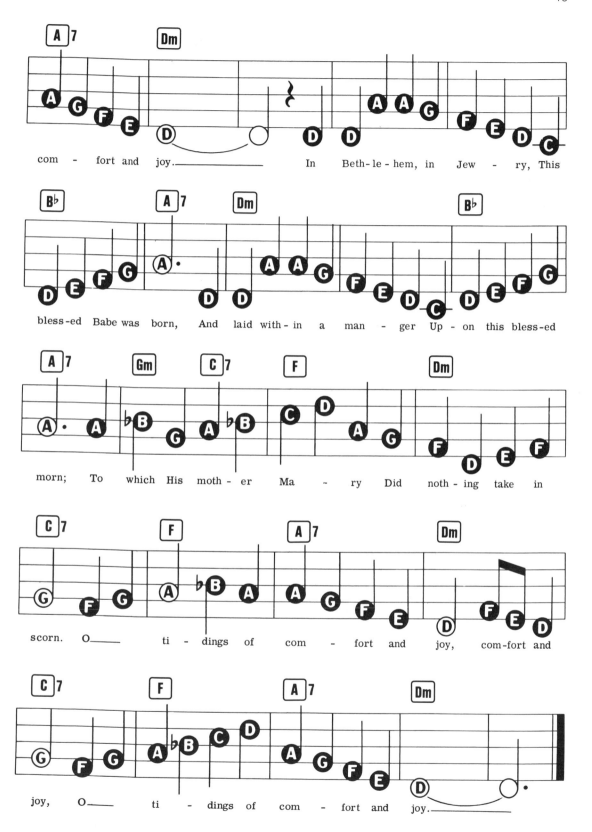

Merry Christmas Everybody

Words & Music:
Neville Holder and James Lea

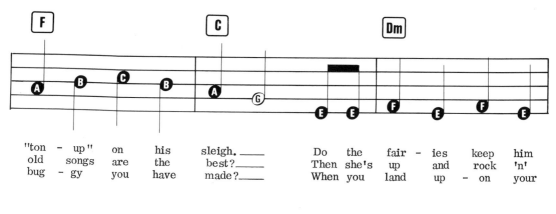

"ton - up" on his sleigh. ____ Do the fair - ies keep him
old songs are the best? ____ Then she's up and rock 'n'
bug - gy you have made? ____ When you land up - on your

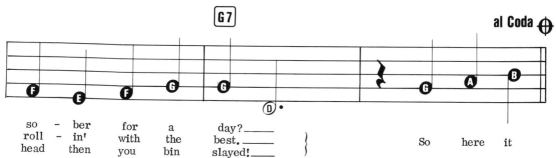

so - ber for a day? ____ So here it
roll - in' with the best. ____
head then you bin slayed! ____

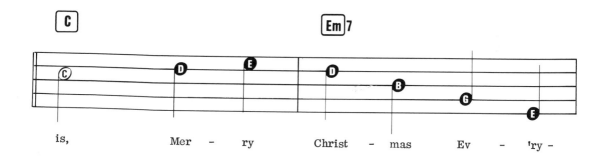

is, Mer - ry Christ - mas Ev - 'ry -

bo - dy's hav - ing fun. Look to the

18

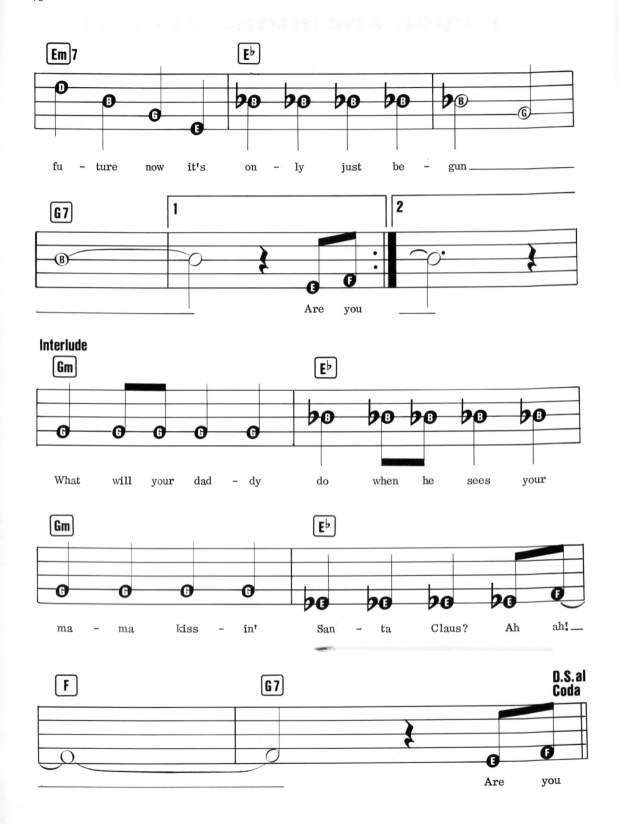

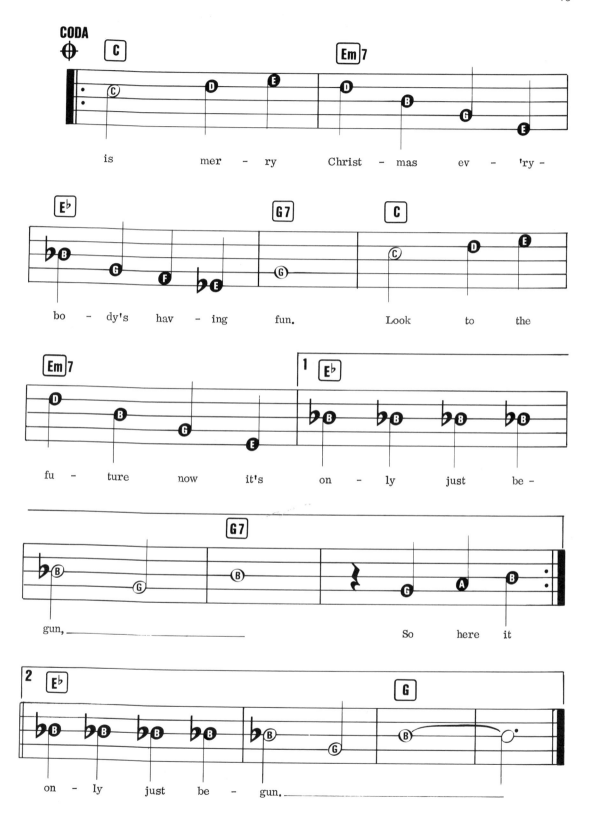

Once In Royal David's City

Traditional

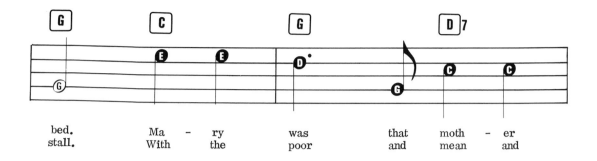

bed.
stall.

	Ma	ry	was	that	moth	er	
	With	the	poor	and	mean	and	

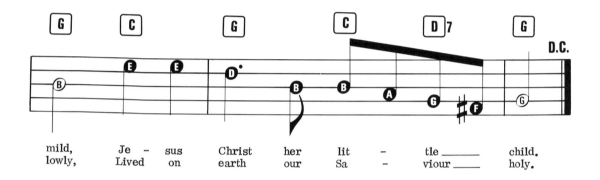

mild,
lowly,

Je	sus	Christ	her	lit	tle	child.
Lived	on	earth	our	Sa	viour	holy.

3. And through all His wondrous childhood,
   He would honour and obey,
   Love and watch the lowly Maiden
   In whose gentle arms He lay;
   Christian children all must be
   Mild, obedient, good as He.

4. For He is in our childhood's pattern,
   Day by day like us He grew;
   He was little, weak and helpless,
   Tears and smiles like us He knew;
   And He feeleth for our sadness,
   And He shareth in our gladness.

5. And our eyes at last shall see Him,
   Through His own redeeming love,
   For that Child so dear and gentle
   Is our Lord in heaven above;
   And He leads His children on
   To the place where He is gone.

6. Not in that poor lowly stable,
   With the oxen standing by,
   We shall see Him; but in heaven,
   Set at God's right hand on high;
   When like stars his children crown'd
   All in white shall wait around.

The First Noel

Traditional

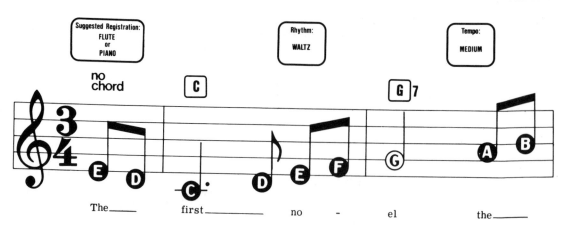

The____ first____ no - el the____

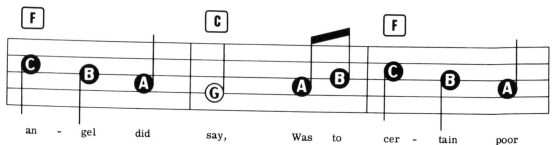

an - gel did say, Was to cer - tain poor

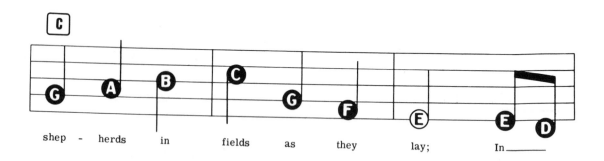

shep - herds in fields as they lay; In____

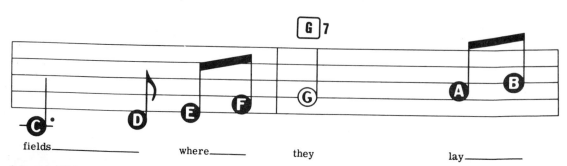

fields____ where____ they lay____

23

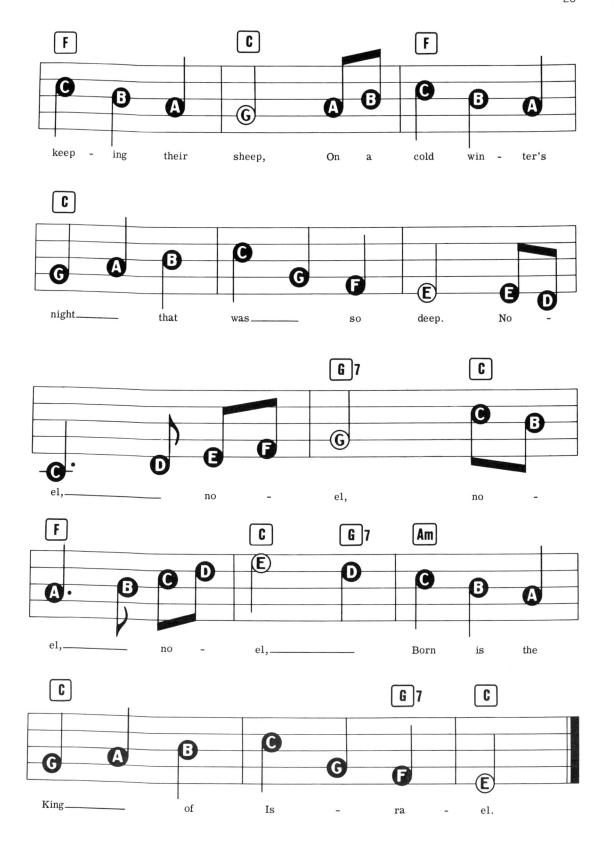

When Santa Got Stuck Up The Chimney

Words & Music:
Jimmy Grafton

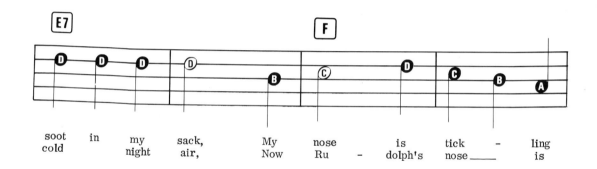

soot   in   my   sack,   My   nose   is   tick - ling
cold   night   air,   Now   Ru - dolph's   nose_____   is

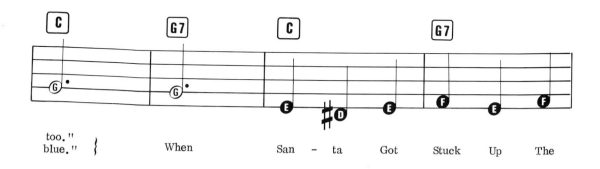

too." }   When   San - ta   Got   Stuck   Up   The
blue."

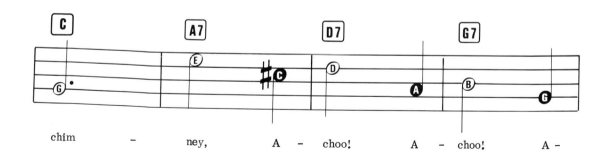

chim - ney,   A - choo!   A - choo!   A-

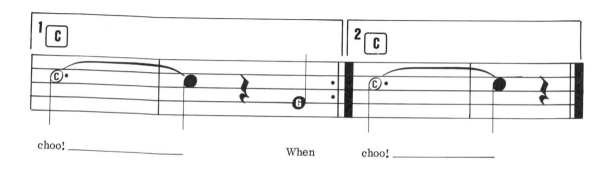

choo! _____   When   choo! _____

We Three Kings Of Orient Are

Traditional

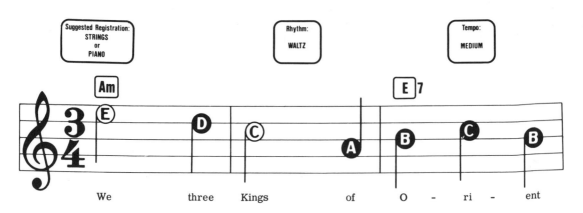

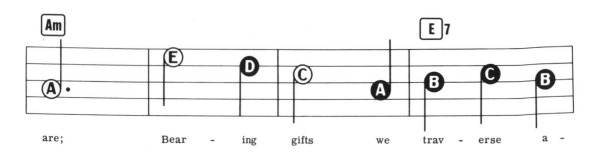

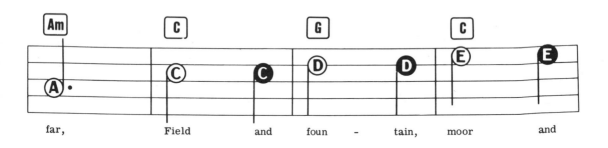

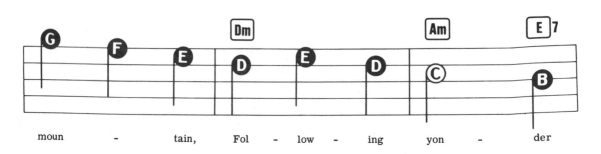

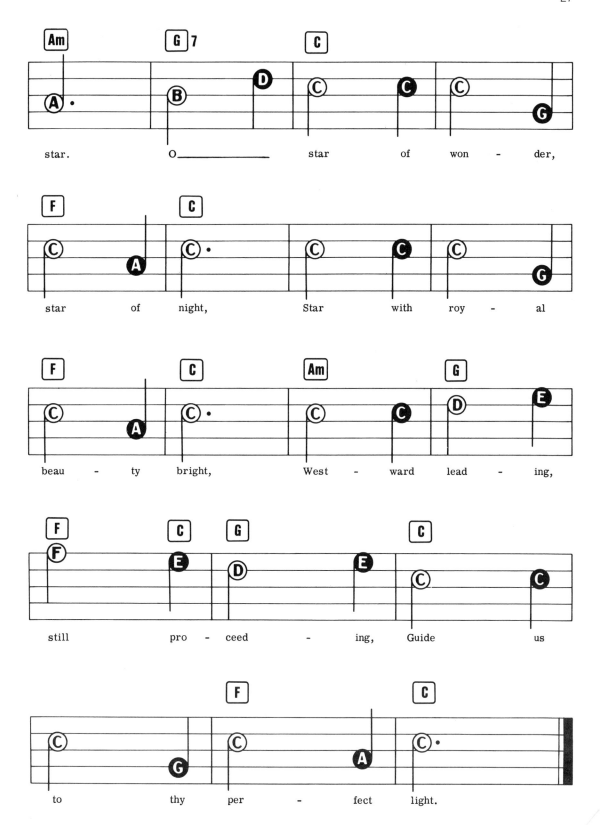

The Twelve Days Of Christmas

Traditional

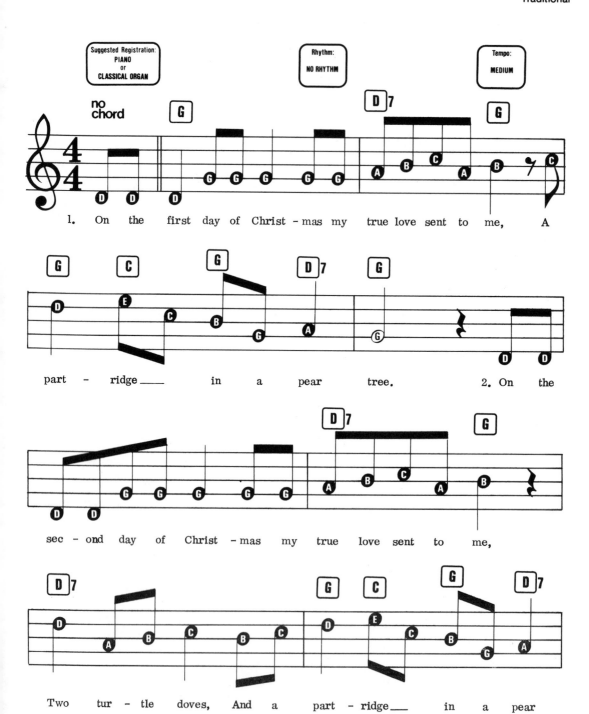

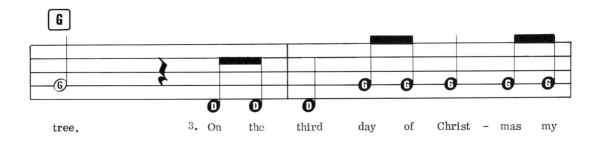

tree.   3. On   the   third   day   of   Christ – mas   my

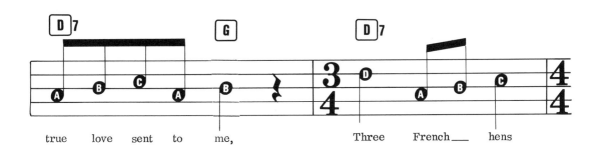

true   love   sent   to   me,   Three   French___   hens

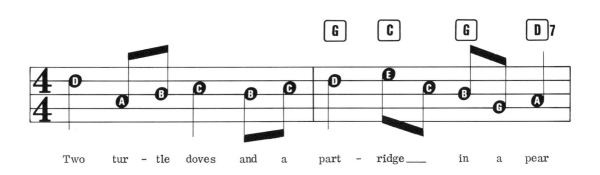

Two   tur – tle   doves   and   a   part – ridge___   in   a   pear

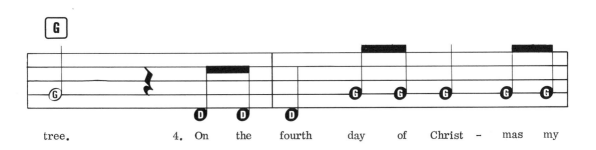

tree.   4. On   the   fourth   day   of   Christ – mas   my

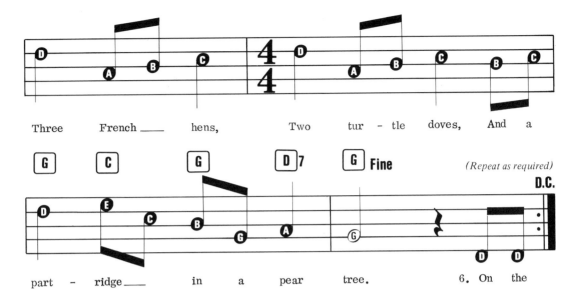

Three French ___ hens, Two tur - tle doves, And a

part - ridge ___ in a pear tree. 6. On the

(Repeat as required)

6. On the sixth day of Christmas
My true love sent to me,
Six geese a-laying,
Five gold rings, etc.

7. On the seventh day of Christmas
My true love sent to me,
Seven swans a-swimming,
Six geese a-laying, etc.

8. On the eighth day of Christmas
My true love sent to me,
Eight maids a-milking,
Seven swans a-swimming, etc.

9. On the ninth day of Christmas
My true love sent to me,
Nine drummers drumming,
Eight maids a-milking, etc.

10. On the tenth day of Christmas
My true love sent to me,
Ten pipers piping,
Nine drummers drumming, etc.

11. On the eleventh day of Christmas
My true love sent to me,
Eleven ladies dancing,
Ten pipers piping, etc.

12. On the twelfth day of Christmas
My true love sent to me,
Twelve lords a-leaping,
Eleven ladies dancing,
Ten pipers piping,
Nine drummers drumming,
Eight maids a-milking,
Seven swans a-swimming,
Six geese a-laying,
Five gold rings,
Four calling birds,
Three French hens,
Two turtle doves,
And a partridge in a pear tree.

It Came Upon The Midnight Clear

Traditional

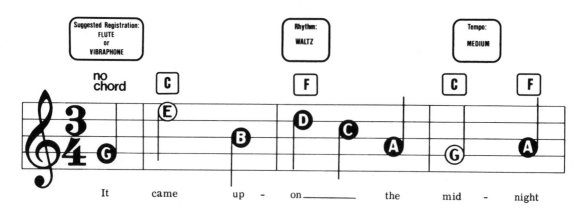

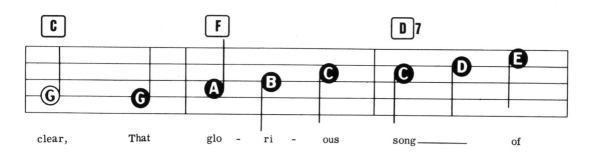

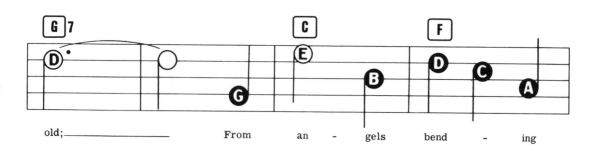

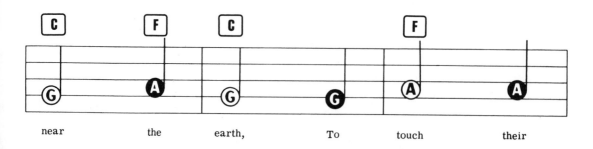

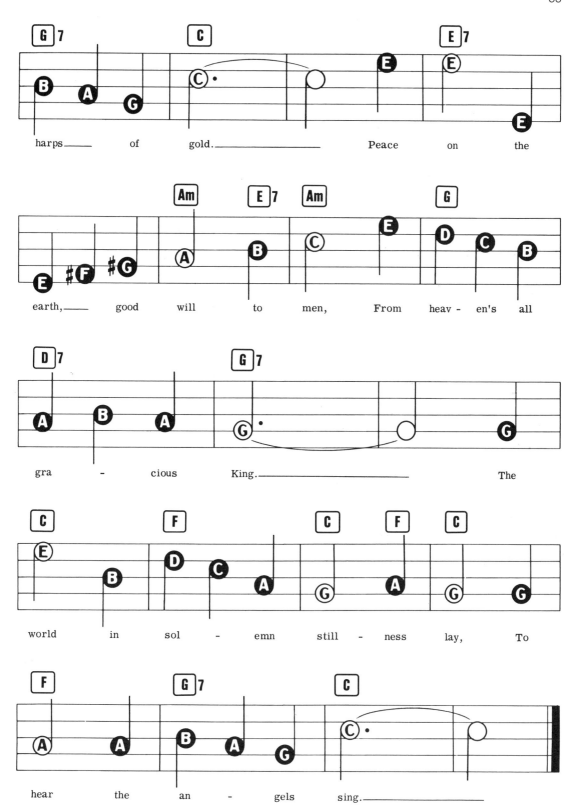

I Believe In Father Christmas

Words & Music:
Peter Sinfield and Greg Lake

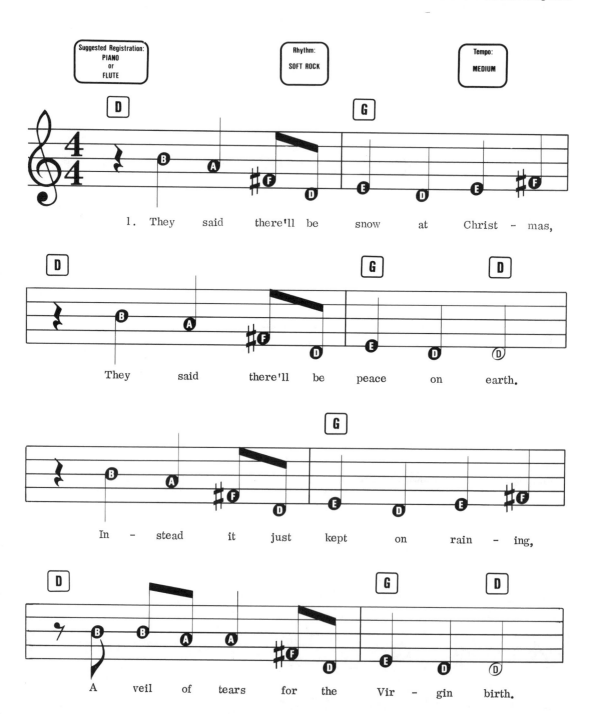

2. They sold me a dream of Christmas,
They sold me a silent night,
And they told me a fairy story,
Till I believed in the Israelite.
And I believed in Father Christmas,
And I looked to the sky with excited eyes,
Till I woke with a yawn in the first light of dawn,
And I saw him through his disguise.

3. I wish you a hopeful Christmas,
I wish you a brave New Year,
All anguish, pain and sadness
Leave your heart and let your road be clear.
They said there'd be snow at Christmas,
They said there'd be peace on earth,
Hallelujah Noel be it heaven or hell,
The Christmas we get we deserve.

Good King Wenceslas

Traditional

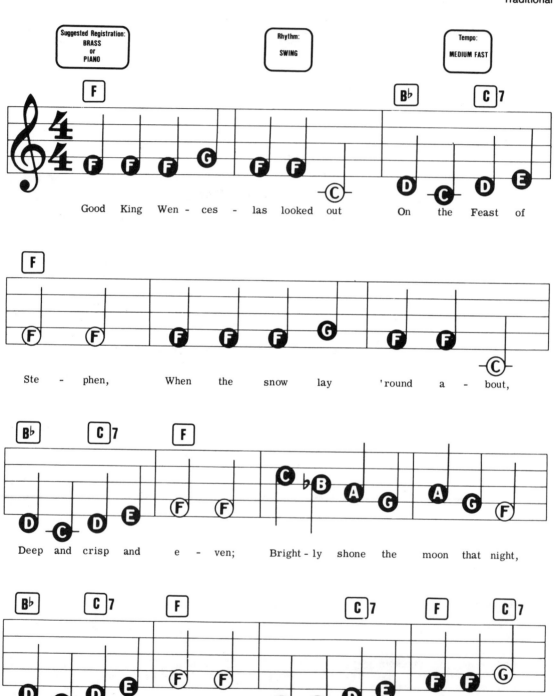

37

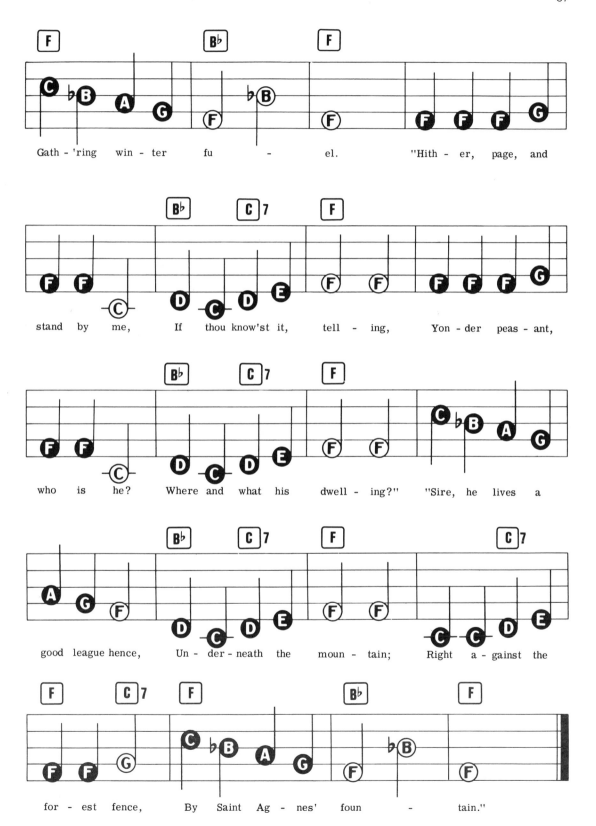

Here Comes Santa Claus

Words & Music:
Gene Autry and Oakley Haldeman

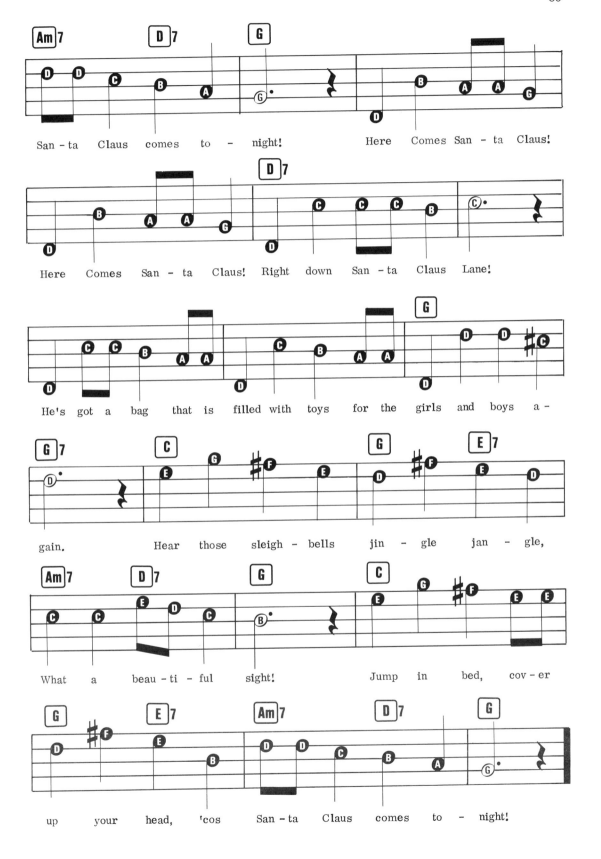

Mary's Boy Child

Words & Music:
Jester Hairston

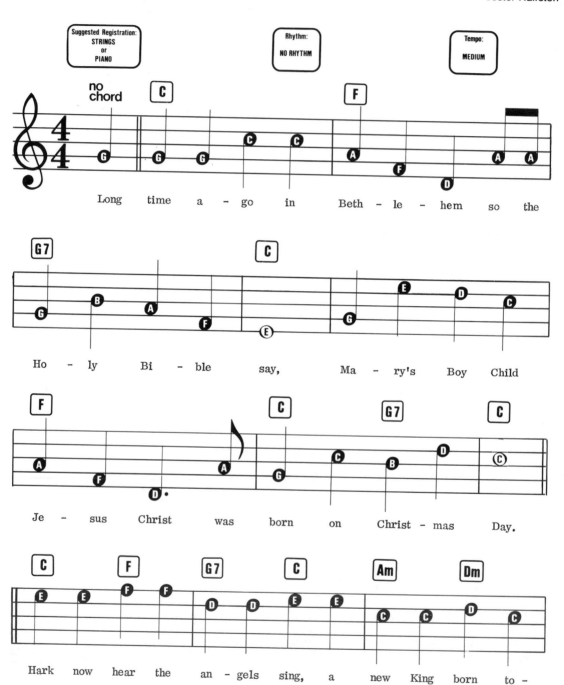

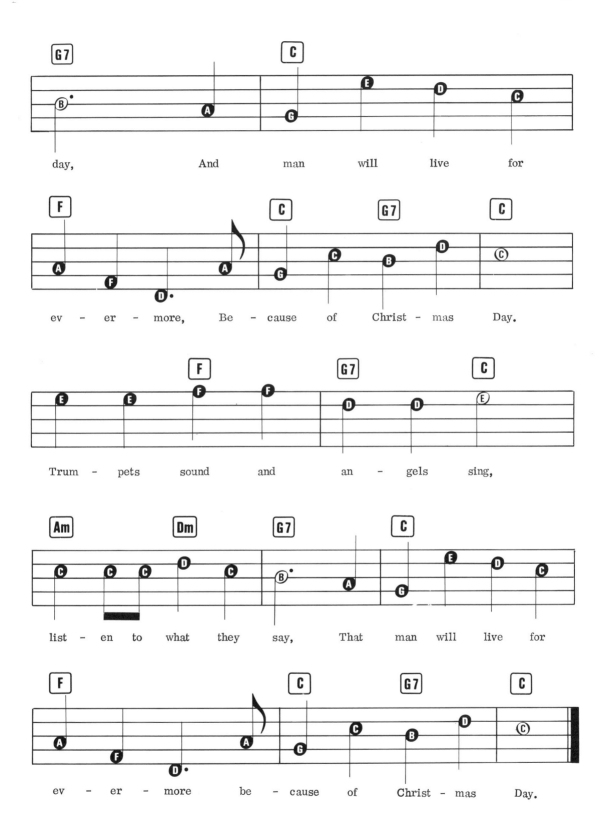

The Holly And The Ivy

Traditional

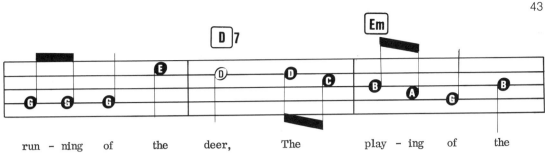

run - ning   of   the   deer,   The   play - ing   of   the

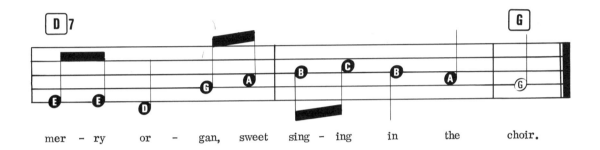

mer - ry   or - gan,   sweet   sing - ing   in   the   choir.

2.   The holly bears a blossom,
       As white as the lily flower,
       And Mary bore sweet Jesus Christ,
       To be our sweet saviour.
           The rising of, etc.

3.   The holly bears a berry,
       As red as any blood,
       And Mary bore sweet Jesus Christ
       To do poor sinners good.
           The rising of, etc.

4.   The holly bears a prickle,
       As sharp as any thorn,
       And Mary bore sweet Jesus Christ
       On Christmas day in the morn.
           The rising of, etc.

5.   The holly bears a bark,
       As bitter as any gall,
       And Mary bore sweet Jesus Christ
       For to redeem us all.
           The rising of, etc.

6.   The holly and the ivy,
       When they are both full grown,
       Of all the trees that are in the wood,
       The holly bears the crown.
           The rising of, etc.

Away In A Manger

Traditional

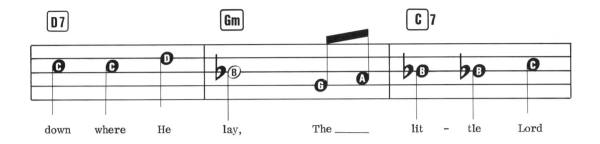

down   where   He   lay,   The ____   lit - tle   Lord

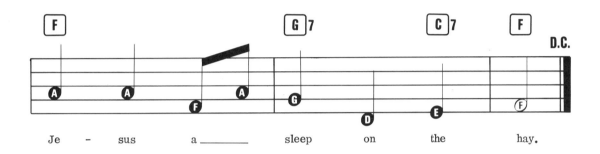

Je - sus   a ____   sleep   on   the   hay.

2. The cattle are lowing,
   The baby awakes,
   But little Lord Jesus,
   No crying He makes.
   I love thee, Lord Jesus,
   Look down from the sky,
   And stay by my side,
   Until morning is nigh.

3. Be near me, Lord Jesus,
   I ask Thee to stay
   Close by me forever,
   And love me I pray.
   Bless all the dear children
   In Thy tender care,
   And fit us for heaven,
   To live with Thee there.

Jingle Bells

Traditional

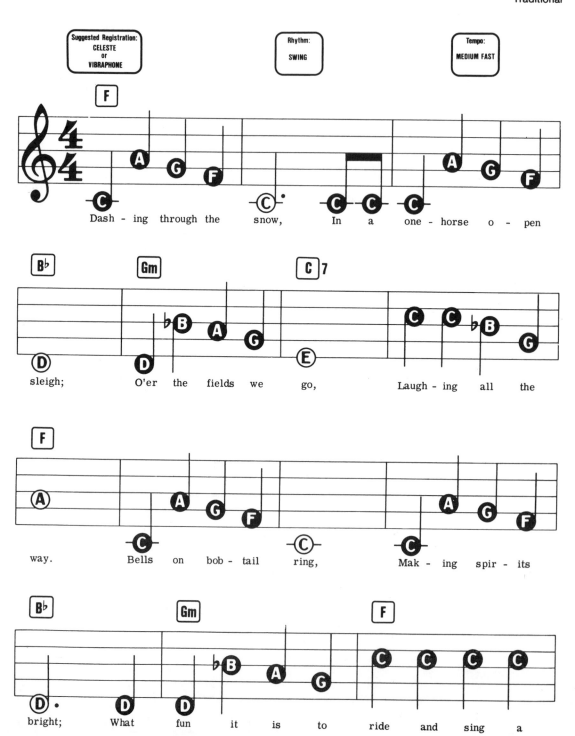

47

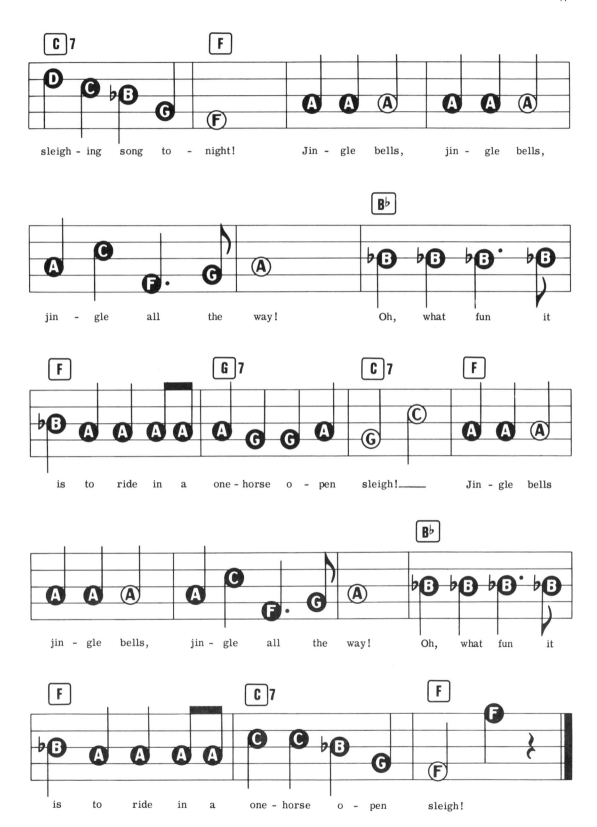

MASTER CHORD CHART

	Major	Minor	Seventh	Minor seventh
C	5 2 1	5 2 1	5 3 2 1	5 3 2 1
C# Db	4 2 1	4 2 1	4 3 2 1	4 3 2 1
D	5 3 1	5 2 1	5 3 2 1	5 3 2 1
Eb	5 3 1	5 3 1	5 3 2 1	5 3 2 1
E	4 3 1	5 3 1	4 3 2 1	5 3 2 1
F	5 3 1	5 3 1	5 3 2 1	5 3 2 1
F# Gb	4 2 1	4 2 1	5 3 2 1	5 3 2 1
G	5 3 1	5 3 1	5 3 2 1	5 3 2 1
Ab	4 2 1	4 2 1	5 4 2 1	5 4 2 1
A	4 2 1	4 2 1	5 4 2 1	5 4 2 1
Bb	4 2 1	4 2 1	5 4 2 1	5 4 2 1
B	4 2 1	4 2 1	4 3 2 1	4 3 2 1

Printed in Great Britain by ETP (E. Anglia) Ltd.